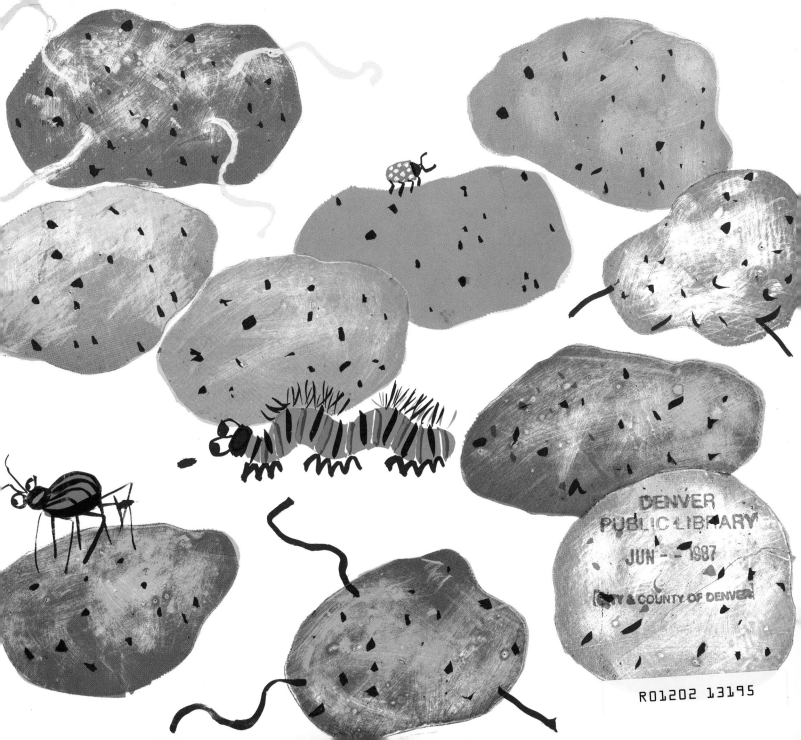

THE HUNGRY LEPRECHAUN

THE HUNGRY LEPRECHAUN

written by
MARY CALHOUN

illustrated by
ROGER DUVOISIN

WILLIAM MORROW AND COMPANY NEW YORK 1962

A shorter version of this story has
appeared in *Humpty Dumpty's Magazine*.

Published simultaneously in the Dominion of
Canada by George J. McLeod Limited, Toronto.

Printed in the United States of America.

Library of Congress Catalog Card Number 62-7214

16 17 18 19 20

Once upon a time, and a very hard time it was, too,
everyone in Ireland was poor.
The Irish ground was so poor
it grew little but rocks and dandelions.
Young Patrick O'Michael O'Sullivan O'Callahan was so poor
he had only dandelion soup to eat.

Even the leprechauns were poor,
not a pot of gold amongst them.
But Patrick O'Michael O'Sullivan O'Callahan didn't know that.
He believed in leprechaun magic,
and he believed that if only he could catch a leprechaun,
he'd be rich.
He'd make the little man give him his gold.
So every day when young Patrick went out
to dig dandelions for dinner,
he watched sharply for a stray leprechaun.
Now the littlest of all little men
lived in a cave under the hill by Patrick's house.
His name was Tippery,
and he was very, *very* hungry.
One day, much as he feared to,
he came out in broad daylight looking for something to eat.

And it happened that Patrick O'Michael was nearby,
digging his dandelions.
Quick, sharp! he spied the little man.
And quick, jump! he flopped his hat over the creature.
He'd caught him!
Patrick O'Michael O'Sullivan O'Callahan
had caught himself a leprechaun!
"Give me your gold, or I'll never let you go,"
ordered Patrick, all eager and gay.
"I haven't any gold, no more than you,"
said Tippery, all miserable and hungry.
"Are dandelions good for eating?"

Then Patrick O'Michael peeked under his hat,
and he saw that he'd caught
the thinnest, the weakest, the most hungry-looking leprechaun
that ever lived.

And he was sorry for the little man.
"Dandelion soup is better than nothing at all,"
he told Tippery.
"I'll take you home and feed you some."
That he did.
Tippery's long, narrow ears perked up
when he saw his bowl of dandelion soup.
He sniffed it with his round nose.
And then he lapped it up with his pointed tongue.

But Patrick O'Michael O'Sullivan O'Callahan
still believed in leprechaun magic,
and he cried, "Whoever heard of a leprechaun
with no magic to make gold! For shame!"
Tippery's long ears drooped.
He'd used up most of his magic in the hard times.
"Come now, where do you keep your magic?" Patrick insisted.
"In your pocket? In your left shoe?"
"In my finger tips, of course," said the leprechaun.
"But I was saving my wee bit for the worst time of all."
"Oho!" Young Patrick sprang up.
"That worst time has come, my little man.
I command you to turn this pot of dandelion soup into gold!"
"I'm still hungry," Tippery complained.
"Will you make more soup if I do?"
Patrick agreed.
Now changing the soup into gold was stirring magic.
But what to stir with?

It had been so long since Tippery had made magic
that he'd almost forgotten how.
He screwed up his nose to think,
and he pulled his left ear.
"Oh me, let me see," he muttered.
Patrick danced about in a dither of eagerness.
"Aha!" said Tippery.
He blew on his fingers to warm up the magic.
Then he stirred the soup with the feather from his cap.
But the dandelion soup only spit at him.

"Maybe—" said Tippery.
He stirred the soup with a broomstraw—
and the dandelions curled up.
"Or was it—?" said Tippery.
He hung over the edge of the pot
and stirred with his long left ear.
The dandelion soup rumbled and roiled.
The dandelions disappeared.

And when the steam cleared,
Tippery had a potful of—frogs!
Little green frogs hopping about.
Tippery's ears hung down.
"I forgot how to make stirring magic," he said.
"Let's dig dandelions and make some more soup."
"No, no. Have faith.
You can do it," urged Patrick O'Michael.

He pointed to the yellow puddle of sunlight on the floor.
"Sure now, you can change that into purest gold," he said.
That was sprinkling magic.
But what to sprinkle with?
The leprechaun bit his pointed tongue,
and he pulled his right ear.
"Oh me, let me see," said Tippery.

"I wonder—" he said.
He dibbled his magic fingers in the puddle of sunlight.
Then he sprinkled it with ashes from the hearth.
The sunlight grew runny.
"It's coming, it's coming!" shouted Patrick O'Michael.
Suddenly it turned into a puddle of water.
Hop, skip, quicker than jump!
The frogs were in the puddle, splashing happily.

Tippery slunk under the table, but Patrick hauled him out.
"Try once more," he begged.
By this time Tippery had used up all of his magic
except what was in one little finger.
Besides, he was very, *very* hungry.
"Let's dig dandelions first," he said.
So Patrick and Tippery went out to the fields
and dug dandelions.

When they had a big pile,
young Patrick pointed to all the rocks in the field.
"If only you could change those rocks into gold," he said.
That was touching magic, hardest kind of all.
Tippery had to get the magic in his little finger
lined up just right and—
there was something he couldn't remember.
"Oh well," said Tippery.
He grabbed both ears and whirled around three times.
He reached his little finger out to the rock,
touched it—
and there was a golden flash!

Quick, fast, Tippery ran about the field
touching rocks with his little finger
until all its magic had run out.
Then Tippery and Patrick O'Michael looked at the rocks.
But not a glitter of gold did they see.
The rocks were still brown.
Wait, there was one thing that glittered—Tippery's finger.
Tippery's little finger had turned into gold!
Oh, the disgrace!
Tippery looked for a place to hide.
"Oh, begorra!" Patrick O'Michael wailed.
"What good is a golden finger?
I *would* catch the most forgetful leprechaun in all Ireland!"

And he gave one of the rocks a mighty whack
with his dandelion shovel.
But what was that?
The rock split open, and it was white inside.
Tippery poked it.
He smelled it with his round nose.
He licked it with his pointed tongue.
"We might try boiling it," he said.
Patrick and Tippery gathered up some of the hard, brown things
and took them home.
They put them in a pot of boiling water.

When the things had cooked,
Patrick and Tippery each took a bite,
and the things were *good!*
"They may not be gold,
but they're good to eat!" shouted Patrick O'Michael.
"Hooray!" cried the little man.
"We put them in the *pot,* and we *ate* them.
We'll call them potatoes!"
Then young Patrick and his leprechaun
had fried potatoes for breakfast,
and baked potatoes for dinner,
and potato soup for supper.
The next day they added dandelion greens to the potatoes
and had potato salad.

But they didn't eat all the potatoes.
Tippery said they must save some to plant.
Which they did.
When the new potatoes sprouted, they gave some to their neighbors,
and then those neighbors gave some to other neighbors.
Soon all Ireland had potatoes.
But to this day, only the children's children of
Patrick O'Michael O'Sullivan O'Callahan
remember that they can thank a hungry leprechaun for potatoes.

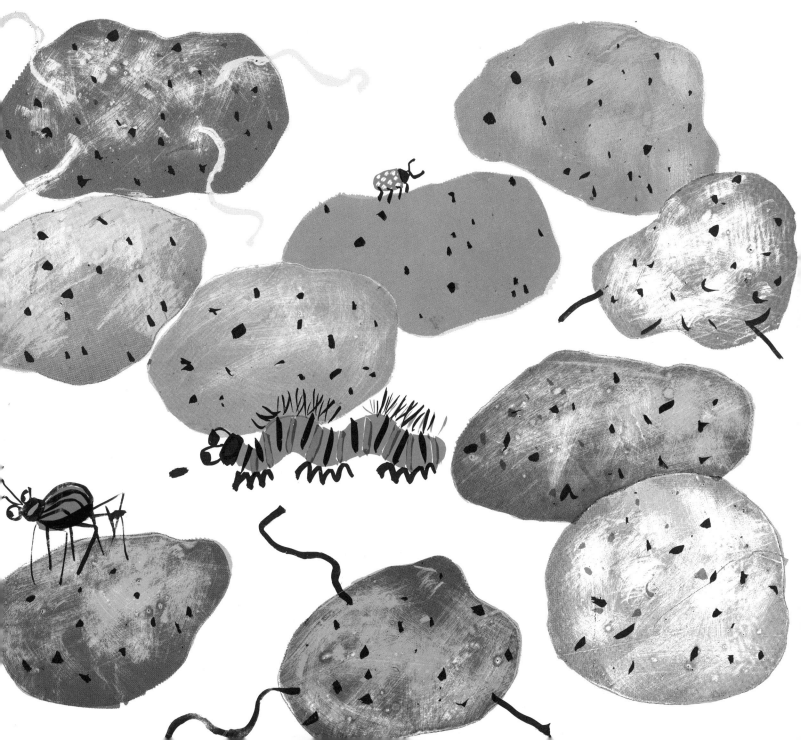

VL

9/24/2002

Grades 4-7

Edith Bolling Galt Wilson

Edith Bolling
Galt Wilson

✦✦✦✦✦✦✦✦✦✦✦✦✦✦✦✦✦✦✦✦✦✦✦✦✦✦

1872–1961

BY ALICE K. FLANAGAN

CHILDREN'S PRESS®
A Division of Grolier Publishing
New York   London   Hong Kong   Sydney
Danbury, Connecticut

Consultant:	LINDA CORNWELL
	Learning Resource Consultant
	Indiana Department of Education

Project Editor:	DOWNING PUBLISHING SERVICES
Page Layout:	CAROLE DESNOES
Photo Researcher:	JAN IZZO

Visit Children's Press on the Internet at:
http://publishing.grolier.com

Library of Congress Cataloging-in-Publication Data
Flanagan, Alice K.
    Edith Bolling Galt Wilson. 1872–1961 / by Alice K. Flanagan
       p. cm. — (Encyclopedia of first ladies)
    Includes bibliographical references and index.
    Summary: Presents a biography of the wife of the twenty-eighth president of
the United States, a woman who helped her husband manage the affairs of his
office after he suffered a stroke.
    ISBN 0-516-20596-X
    1. Wilson, Edith Bolling Galt. 1872–1961—Juvenile literature. 2. Presidents'
spouses—United States—Biography—Juvenile literature. [1. Wilson, Edith
Bolling Galt, 1872–1961. 2. First ladies.] I. Title II. Series
E767.3.W55   1998
973.91'3'092—dc21   98–7893
[B]   CIP
                                              AC

Table of Contents

Edith Bolling Galt Wilson

A Strong Woman

☆ ☆ ☆ ☆ ☆ ☆ ☆ ☆ ☆ ☆ ☆ ☆ ☆ ☆ ☆ ☆

Edith Bolling Galt Wilson became First Lady during a critical time in history. World War I was raging in Europe. The United States was on the brink of war. And the president of the United States—the most powerful man in the world—was struggling to recover from the death of his first wife.

Before marrying Woodrow Wilson, Edith Bolling Galt ran a successful business. After becoming Mrs. Wilson and the nation's First Lady, Edith immersed herself in her husband's work. Often, politicians and reporters criticized her for spending too much time with him.

☆ ☆ ☆ ☆ ☆ ☆ ☆ ☆ ☆ ☆ ☆ ☆ ☆ ☆ ☆ ☆

When the president suffered a stroke during his second term in office and required complete rest, Edith supervised his workload. From October 1919 to April 1920, she alone decided who would see the president and what he was told. She decided when to share the president's decisions on important matters with cabinet members, congressional staff, and the press. During this time, some newspapers called her the "first woman president."

Unlike many First Ladies who used their position to influence fashion or promote women's rights and favorite causes, Edith Bolling did not pursue her own special interests in the White House. The president remained her only concern. Her loving care of him extended his life and the influence he had on the world stage. Perhaps at no other time in U.S. history was the presence of such a strong woman so necessary to a president as he led other nations of the world on a course toward peace.

This marriage license application, signed and dated on December 16, 1915, authorized the marriage of Woodrow Wilson and Edith Bolling Galt.

After her husband Norman Galt's death, Edith Bolling Galt became the sole owner of the successful Galt family jewelry and fine silver business in Washington, D.C.

☆ ☆ ☆ ☆ ☆ ☆ ☆ ☆ ☆ ☆ ☆ ☆ ☆ ☆

11

CHAPTER ONE

The Bolling Family

✶ ✶ ✶ ✶ ✶ ✶ ✶ ✶ ✶ ✶ ✶ ✶ ✶ ✶ ✶ ✶

Edith Bolling was born on October 15, 1872, in the small Virginia town of Wytheville. She was the seventh of eleven children born to William Holcombe Bolling and his wife Sallie White Bolling. The other children were Rolfe, Gertrude, Annie Lee, Will, Bertha, Charles, Randolph, Wilmer, Julian, and Geraldine. (Charles and Geraldine died in infancy.)

Edith's father was a well-known circuit court judge. Her mother was a genteel Southern woman. The Bollings were once a prosperous family. They traced their ancestry to the seventeenth-century Jamestown, Virginia, settlement. There, in 1614, British captain

✶ ✶ ✶ ✶ ✶ ✶ ✶ ✶ ✶ ✶ ✶ ✶ ✶ ✶ ✶ ✶

Portrait of America, 1872: Reconstructing America

✮ ✮

Edith Bolling was born into an America under reconstruction. The Civil War had been over for seven years. But it had left the country confused. Making equality real for former slaves proved easier said than done. While all the Southern states had come back into the Union, *Reconstruction,* a set of policies to reform and rebuild the war-torn South, was failing. Laws passed to enact equality and protect the voting rights of newly freed black men left American women behind since they still couldn't vote. The Ku Klux Klan rode by night to terrorize and discourage blacks from voting and living free, although by 1872, anti-Klan laws had reduced the violence.

Nevertheless, a new America rose from the confusion. Industry boomed, and for the first time, more Americans worked in factories than on farms. After the war, 3 million new immigrants arrived from Europe seeking their fortunes. Many joined the pioneers pushing westward. Unfortunately, new beginnings for these settlers meant ruin for the Native Americans whose lands they wanted.

Elsewhere in this new America, the first woman to graduate from law school was an African-American named Charlotte E. Ray. And even though women still couldn't vote, the first woman ran for president on the ticket of the Equal Rights Party. Her challenge barely affected Ulysses S. Grant, however, who was elected to a second term, despite scandal and corruption in his administration.

Other interesting events helped to reconstruct America in 1872. Congress created Yellowstone, the country's first national park, to preserve some wilderness. Roller skating became a fad, and the first modern typewriter keyboard—called QWERTY for the top row of letters—was invented. Gum made from chicle, a Mexican tree sap, gave American chewers a new option besides wax or tobacco. And Aaron Montgomery Ward gave people a new way to shop—through the mail.

From slavery to freedom, from Europe to America, from farm to factory, and from east to west, Americans in 1872 worked hard to reconstruct a new way of life.

John Rolfe and Pocahontas, the daughter of Chief Wahunsonacook of the Powhatan tribe, were married. When Edith Bolling was born, she was a ninth-generation descendant of Pocahontas.

Before the Civil War, the Bollings owned a plantation with many slaves. After the war, they were like hundreds of other plantation owners who had lost everything. Without slaves to work for them, they closed up their plantations and moved into town.

The Bollings moved into an old brick house in Wytheville, which had been owned by the family for a long time. It had been used as a Confederate hospital during the war and needed a lot of repairs. It took the Bollings several years to make the house comfortable. At times, it seemed too small for the family, which included eleven

Pocahontas (c. 1595–1617)

☆ ☆

Pocahontas

The daughter of the chief of the Powhatan Indians was by all accounts a remarkable young woman. Familiar to us as Pocahontas (a nickname meaning "frisky"), her real name was Matowaka. She did much to promote good relations between her people and the English settlers of Virginia. Having saved Captain John Smith from her father's deadly wrath, she is depicted in song and story as being in love with Smith. However, Pocahontas was only twelve years old at the time. She married colonist John Rolfe at age seventeen, which pleased her father and encouraged peace. John took her to England, where she was baptized and changed her name to Rebecca. The toast of London, Pocahontas even met the queen. Sadly, she soon died of smallpox, leaving a small son.

children, both grandmothers, and two of Mrs. Bolling's sisters.

As a child, Edith spent a lot of time with her grandmother, who was an invalid. Grandmother Bolling suffered from a spinal injury she had received as a child. The condition kept her confined to her room and required constant care. Nevertheless, she managed to rule the household with a firm hand.

Edith slept in Grandmother Bolling's room and cared for all her needs. She always kept her informed of family business. As a reward, Grandmother Bolling showered Edith with attention. She taught her to read, write, knit, sew dresses, and speak French.

Edith Bolling (second from right) at the age of three with some of her brothers and sisters

William Holcombe Bolling, Edith's father

Sallie White Bolling, Edith's mother

Until the age of thirteen, Edith lived at home. Her parents did not have enough money to send all their children to formal school at the same time, so they taught several of them at home. Edith's parents and Grandmother Bolling taught her everything she knew. Sometimes, a tutor or governess helped them. Edith rarely played with children other than her brothers and sisters. She didn't leave the town of Wytheville until she attended formal school.

17

Edith's father was a stern but loving man. Each evening, he would read aloud from Shakespeare, Dickens, and other classics. He took time out of his busy schedule to teach his children their numbers and the Bible.

Edith's mother was a frail woman but strong enough to give birth to eleven children and manage a busy household. She married Mr. Bolling before she was eighteen years old and afterward led a sheltered life. Mrs. Bolling was much younger than her husband and yielded to his strong personality. She felt secure under his protection. According to Edith, she was "radiantly happy" despite having less than she needed to raise a large family adequately. She remained totally loyal to her husband, who was her life.

In 1887, Edith was sent to a small boarding school in Virginia, to be "finished," as her father would say. But she stayed only a year. The school didn't provide adequate heat and food for the students, so Edith's parents refused to send her back the following year.

Two years later, Edith enrolled at Powell's School in Richmond, Virginia. Once again, however, she did

This photograph of Edith was taken when she was at boarding school in Virginia.

not stay long. In May of 1890, Mr. Powell suffered an accident and had to close the school. Edith looked forward to returning to school the following winter, but her father sent her three younger brothers instead. Edith's parents considered Edith, who was then eighteen, "ready for the world." She could do all the things expected of a young, refined lady of the 1890s. She could read, write, do numbers, play

Richmond, Virginia, as it looked about 1890 when Edith attended boarding school there

the piano, and sing. She knew her Bible well, had good morals, and could manage a household.

Confident that Edith was ready for marriage, Edith's parents sent her to Washington, D.C., to stay with her oldest sister, Gertrude, and, her husband, Alexander Hunter Galt. Gertrude introduced Edith to Washington's social life. She taught her the proper way to act at the theater, the opera, and dinner parties where there were many young men.

Sometime during her four-month

Part of Edith's finishing-school training included singing and playing the piano.

19

A photograph of Edith taken during her first trip to Washington, D.C.

The Capitol has always been a favorite destination for visitors to Washington, D.C.

visit in Washington, Edith met Norman Galt, her brother-in-law's cousin. Norman, who was twenty-seven at the time, was a junior partner in his family's jewelry and fine silver store in Washington, D.C.

Norman was captivated with Edith, who by this time was quite an attractive young lady. He visited her frequently the final week before she went home. The following fall, when Edith returned to Washington, she and Norman resumed their friendship. Over the next four years, Norman dated Edith and waited patiently for her to be interested in marriage. But Edith was not "head over heels" in love with Norman and didn't want to marry anyone.

The more Norman was around, however, the more Edith had to admit that he was good for her. He came

An afternoon stroll along the capital's Connecticut Avenue was a popular pastime in the 1890s.

Tourists in the Great Rotunda of the Capitol in Washington, D.C., admire the dome.

from a well-to-do family and showed a lot of interest in her family.

Edith once wrote that Norman "was sound in his judgments, and unfailing in his eagerness to help the younger boys and do everything he could for anyone I loved." He also seemed to have a secure future ahead. Because of these positive attributes, when Norman asked Edith to marry him in 1896, Edith said yes.

An 1890s view of the White House, the Treasury, and Pennsylvania Avenue

CHAPTER TWO

Young Mrs. Galt

☆ ☆ ☆ ☆ ☆ ☆ ☆ ☆ ☆ ☆ ☆ ☆ ☆ ☆ ☆ ☆ ☆

Edith was twenty-four in 1896 when she married Norman Galt. He was thirty-two. After the wedding, Edith and Norman moved in with Norman's father until they were able to afford their own house. The first few years in their new home were happy ones. Then tragedy struck. First, Norman's brother-in-law died. Only twenty-four hours later, Norman's father died. Then, within months, Norman's older brother Charlie became an invalid. Within the span of a year, Norman found himself in charge of the family business. He was only thirty-five.

Edith, too, took on more family responsibilities when

☆ ☆ ☆ ☆ ☆ ☆ ☆ ☆ ☆ ☆ ☆ ☆ ☆ ☆ ☆ ☆ ☆

her father died suddenly in 1899. Following his death, Edith's mother and younger siblings looked to her for financial help. They depended on her to make all the family decisions.

As the years passed, life returned to normal in the Galt household. Edith and Norman looked forward to the birth of their first child. In September 1903, Edith gave birth to a baby boy. He was not well, however, and lived only three days. Edith was devastated by the death of her baby and remained hospitalized due to complications stemming from his birth. Afterward, she could no longer have children. Edith kept the birth and death of her infant son a family secret all of her life. Only after her death did it become public knowledge.

Faced with the fact that she could no longer have children, Edith turned to interests outside the home. She began visiting her family more often and spent more time shopping and attending the theater. For the next three years, she lived an active, independent lifestyle. Little did Edith know how helpful being independent

would be to her when tragedy struck her life again.

In January 1908, Norman died after a brief illness. All at once, Edith became sole owner of the Galt business. Lacking a business background, Edith thought hard about what she should do. She felt responsible for the

After Norman's death in 1908, Edith became the sole owner of the Galt jewelry business.

future of the employees. Her own three brothers had only recently been hired at Galts, and her mother and sister were financially dependent on them.

Relying on her own ability to learn quickly, Edith decided to keep the business and run it herself. She left the day-to-day operations in the capable hands of the store managers. With the aid of a lawyer friend, she reviewed the accounts regularly. For the next four years, she followed her instincts in running the business. It paid off. In no time, Edith was drawing a good income to support herself and her family.

Although the business was running smoothly, Edith was lonely without Norman. One or another of her brothers and sisters had offered to live with her. But Edith felt it was best for everyone if she remained independent. After all, she was still young and attractive at thirty-six years old. And she would very likely marry again.

Feeling financially secure, Edith began traveling abroad. Every year, she visited Europe with one of her sisters

In 1912, Edith traveled to Europe with her sister Bertha (above).

or a female relative or friend. Of all her companions, Edith most enjoyed traveling with Alice Gertrude Gordon, whom she fondly called "Altrude."

In 1912, Edith took her sister Bertha with her to Europe. She returned to news of President Woodrow Wilson's election. Edith's sister-in-law, Annie Litchfield, had worked in Woodrow

Worth the Trip

On a trip to Europe, women of Edith Galt's status would not pass up the opportunity to shop for new clothes, and Edith was no exception. However, such an errand would not have much in common with a trip to the mall today. In Paris, Edith frequented the House of Worth. This elegant dressmaker dictated what all women of high society—including Empress Eugenie of France, the queen regent of Portugal, and all the richest American ladies—wore for the last half of the nineteenth century. This establishment in Paris looked more like an embassy than a store. Ladies gained entry only with a reference from another of Mr. Worth's clients. Young men dressed in black uniforms escorted visitors through a series of rooms piled high with luxurious silks, velvets, and woolens. Only then did the shopper enter the display room, where gowns hung on wooden forms. If a gown took her fancy, the visitor could try it on and step into the *salon de lumière*, specially fitted with mirrors and gaslights to produce an evening atmosphere. She then might order a gown or two made from the fabrics of her choice.

Wilson's election campaign. She was a staunch Wilson supporter and tried getting Edith involved, but Edith was not interested in politics. To satisfy Annie, however, she read several of Wilson's speeches and once took her mother to hear the president speak.

In 1914, Edith decided to spend a summer vacation with her friend Altrude in New Hampshire. The vacation did not turn out as Edith had expected, but it did set in motion a series of events that eventually brought Edith and President Woodrow Wilson together.

Edith and Altrude had decided to vacation in New Hampshire because Doctor Cary Grayson was going to be vacationing nearby. Grayson, who was dating Altrude at the time, was a longtime acquaintance of Edith's. He was also President Wilson's physician.

Governor Wilson accepted the Democratic nomination for president at Sea Girt, his home in New Jersey.

Dr. Cary Grayson, President Wilson's physician, is shown here as a rear admiral in 1919.

Harlakenden House

★ ★

Beginning in 1913, the Wilsons rented this mansion from its owner Winston Churchill to use as a summer home. Although the president could not often get away from the capital, Ellen Wilson and the Wilson daughters enjoyed the rambling house on a scenic overlook above the Connecticut River in Cornish, New Hampshire. The artistically inclined Ellen particularly liked the neighbors at Cornish, many of whom were among the country's most notable artists. The great sculptor Augustus Saint-Gaudens owned a house named Aspet and Maxfield Parrish, a reknowned illustrator, called his Cornish home The Oaks.

Grayson and the Wilson family were to spend the summer at Harlakenden, the Wilsons' rented house in Cornish, New Hampshire. Edith and Altrude eagerly awaited their arrival. But a crisis in Europe delayed the president's plans. One week followed the next without any sign of Wilson and Grayson. Finally, Edith and Altrude learned that the president's trip had been canceled because Mrs. Wilson had died. A few days later, war broke out in Europe.

Realizing that Cary Grayson would not be joining them for the rest of the summer, Edith and Altrude proceeded with their own plans. They resumed their hiking and canoeing trip. Toward the end of their stay, Edith ate some spoiled food and suffered a serious bout of ptomaine poisoning. With great effort, she finally made it home to Washington, D.C., where she received immediate care.

Dr. Grayson stopped by to see Edith every day. He spoke about the war and how lonely the president had become since his wife died. Edith could see how worried Grayson was. If Mr. Wilson didn't shake off his sadness soon, it would seriously affect his job as president. Dr. Grayson was concerned about other people in the White House, too. Helen Bones, who

Ellen Louise Axson Wilson (1860–1914)

✮ ✮

The first Wilson First Lady, Ellen Axson Wilson, was in many ways very different from Edith Bolling Galt. Born in Savannah, Georgia, Ellen spent her Civil War childhood in towns around the South. She graduated from a women's college in Georgia and went on to study art in New York City. Well-read in literature and philosophy, Ellen's first love was painting, and she had considerable artistic talent. She and Woodrow married in 1885. His career as college professor and president at Princeton University and the raising of their three daughters took them to 1910 when he became governor of New Jersey. Ellen actively worked to get her husband elected president in 1912, and as First Lady was more interested in helping Washington's poor than in hobnobbing with high society. She

Ellen Wilson

lobbied Congress to pass a bill to clear many of the city's slums. Never before had a president's wife committed such time and effort to social reform. Ellen was known for her intellect, kindness, and dignity. The president relied heavily on her, and when she died at the age of fifty-four of kidney disease, she left behind a lonely and forlorn Woodrow Wilson.

President Wilson with his first wife, Ellen, and their three daughters

29

was the president's cousin and Mrs. Wilson's personal secretary, was also lonely and needed companionship.

Thinking that Edith and Helen might like each other, Dr. Grayson asked Edith if he could bring Helen to visit her sometime. Edith, however, did not want to get involved in official Washington circles. She told Dr. Grayson to bring Helen to visit Altrude instead.

Dr. Grayson would not be put off by Edith's decision not to get involved in the White House. One day he arrived at her house with the president's daughter, Mrs. Nell McAdoo, and Helen Bones. He asked Edith to join them for a ride through the park. She could not refuse.

During the pleasant afternoon in the park, Edith learned that she had much in common with Helen. A day or two later, Miss Bones and Mrs. McAdoo came again. Other visits with Helen Bones soon followed. And so began Edith's weekly visits with Helen that became such a part of both of their lives. The routine included a

Left: Nell McAdoo, Woodrow
Wilson's youngest daughter

Above: Helen Bones, who was the president's
cousin and had been Ellen Wilson's personal
secretary, became one of Edith's close friends.

Nothing New: Electric Automobiles

★ ★

A 1905 picture of Edith in her electric car

In 1900, about 8,000 cars were manufactured in the United States, and electricity powered nearly a third of them. Gasoline-powered cars were loud and dirty and required hand-cranking (a difficult task) to start. Electrics, however, ran slowly and for only about 50 miles (80 km) on one charge. Such drawbacks didn't bother the wealthy women of leisure who bought them. To young adventurers bent on touring the country's expanding roadways, however, the electric's short range and day-long recharging time were impractical. Besides, the clatter and ruggedness of gas cars added to the fun. After Henry Ford introduced the popular gas-powered Model T in 1908, and Charles Kettering perfected an electric starter to replace the troublesome crank, electric cars began to disappear. Today, the government and popular opinion demand that the automobile industry help clean up the air by producing autos that do not pollute. General Motors has promised to have an electric automobile ready to go into mass production by 2004, and other manufacturers have joined the race to put affordable and practical electrics back in the showroom.

Edith Galt and Helen Bones drove each week to Rock Creek Park (above), where they took long walks before returning to Edith's house for tea.

drive to the park in Edith's electric car, followed by a long walk. Then the two friends would return to Edith's house for tea. During their visits, Edith learned a lot about the Wilson family, especially Helen's "Cousin Woodrow." She felt herself intimately drawn to the lonely man who bore the terrible burdens of the presidential office.

☆ ☆ ☆ ☆ ☆ ☆ ☆ ☆ ☆ ☆ ☆ ☆ ☆ ☆ ☆ ☆

CHAPTER THREE

A White House Romance

One afternoon in March 1915, Helen and Edith went on their usual walk through the park. However, instead of using Edith's car, the two were driven in the White House car. After their long walk on the muddy paths, Edith suggested that they return home to clean up before having tea. Helen insisted that they have their tea at the White House.

After hearing that the president and Dr. Grayson were playing golf and would not be at the White House when they arrived, Edith agreed to have tea with Helen. One can imagine her surprise, however, when, after getting off the elevator on the second floor

Thomas Woodrow Wilson (1856–1924)

✫ ✫

Born in Virginia in 1856, Woodrow Wilson's childhood set him on course to be among history's greatest peacemakers. His minister father's daily teachings and discussions gave him great religious faith and an ability to express his ideas. Personal memories of the horrors of the Civil War, which raged through the South

President Woodrow Wilson

during his early childhood, undoubtedly fueled his presidential desire to promote world peace. Unable to read until the age of nine, Woodrow, who went by his first name of Thomas until college, found school difficult but was always ready to organize his fellow students into various clubs and organizations. After earning a law degree and practicing law, he decided on a scholar's life and returned to school, first as a professor, then to teach, and finally to administer Princeton, the college he had attended. Before becoming the United States president who wanted to "make the world safe for democracy," Woodrow Wilson was the college president who tried to eliminate elite social clubs based on class and wealth and to establish a more democratic atmosphere on campus.

of the White House, she saw Dr. Grayson and the president coming toward her. Shocked, Edith stood there frozen in her muddy boots and black tailored suit from Paris.

After nervous small talk, the four cleaned up and went into the oval sitting room. There, around a crackling fire, they shared the interesting events of their day. As dinner approached, Edith declined the president's invitation to join them. She said she would come back on a day she felt more suitably dressed. Quickly, that day came.

On March 23, Edith returned to the White House for dinner. After a pleasant evening, Edith left favorably impressed with Mr. Wilson. In a letter to her sister-in-law, Annie Litchfield, Edith described her impressions of the president. He is "perfectly charming," she said, "and one of the easiest and most delightful hosts I have ever known."

Similar evenings at the White House followed. By the end of April, Edith was a nightly dinner guest. Usually, before or after dinner, Edith, Helen, and the president took a ride in the White House car. They drove with the top down. In the open air, the president unburdened himself with talk of the war in Europe and other world crises.

Edith kept up her daily afternoon walks with Helen. Sometimes, Woodrow's daughters, Nell and Margaret, joined them. They liked Edith and could see how much happiness she

Woodrow Wilson's daughter Margaret

Being taken for a drive in an open car was always one of President Wilson's favorite ways to relax. Here he is shown with his first wife, Ellen, and others.

had brought to their family since their mother died. Everyone noticed how quickly Edith and Woodrow were becoming romantically involved.

By May 4, Woodrow told Edith he loved her. Edith was shocked by his declaration and told him that it was impossible that he could love her. In Edith's memoirs she reveals their conversation to one another: "You don't really know me," she told Woodrow. "And it's less than a year since your wife died." Woodrow replied, ". . . in this place, time is not measured by weeks, or months, or years, but by deep human experience; and since her death I have lived a lifetime of loneliness and heartache. I was afraid, knowing you, I would shock you but I would be less than a gentleman if I continued to make opportunities to see you without telling you . . . that I want you to be my wife."

Edith was not quite ready to say yes to Woodrow's marriage proposal. After a week went by, however, she had changed her mind. She gave a letter to Woodrow just as he was leaving for a speaking engagement in Philadelphia.

In the letter, Edith said that previously she had thought love was no longer possible for her. But since Woodrow had told her that he loved her, she wanted to give their relationship a try. She said, "We both deserve the right to try and if you, with your wonderful love, can quicken that which has lain dead so long within me, I promise not to shut it out of my heart, but to bid it welcome, and come to you with the joy of it in my eyes."

While Edith and Woodrow spent most of their time courting and thinking about each other, world problems mounted. There was trouble in Mexico. U.S. Marines had taken control of Haiti. War raged in Europe. And people were starving in Russia. In response to all the turmoil, the United States began preparing for war.

Amid all the depressing events surrounding Edith and Woodrow, their love blossomed. Even when they could not be together, they strengthened their relationship through letters. Edith and Woodrow wrote to each other daily, sometimes as many as twenty handwritten pages. In the

Something to Talk About

✦ ✦

As Edith and Woodrow discovered, Americans delight in gossip. And they especially love to talk about the private lives and habits of famous people, including the president and First Lady. Presidential gossip has a long history. To this day, people still talk about whether the third president, Thomas Jefferson, had a love affair with a slave named Sally Hemings. Thirty-five years before becoming the dynamic and popular seventh president, Andrew Jackson married Rachel Robards. When the couple wed, they mistakenly believed Rachel's divorce to be final. Political enemies dug up the story, and made it a campaign issue. Both Presidents Andrew Johnson and Theodore Roosevelt were accused—unjustly, it seems—of drinking too much. In 1886, presidential gossip reached a fever pitch when Grover Cleveland,

Andrew Jackson

Rachel Robards Jackson

age forty-eight, married the beautiful Frances Folsom, twenty-seven years younger, in a White House wedding. The public adored Frances and talked endlessly about her. Many speculated that Cleveland treated her badly, which appears to have been completely untrue. Naturally, the courtship of Woodrow and Edith generated dozens of rumors. Some gossipers even whispered that the president had actually murdered his first wife.

Frances Folsom Cleveland

Grover Cleveland

letters, Woodrow expressed his feelings for Edith. He also talked about his work. Often, he sent her classified papers with his written comments on them. He wanted her to understand the political issues confronting him and to help him deal with the problems taking up so much of his time.

Early in September 1915, Edith and Woodrow were engaged. Both

agreed to wait until after the 1916 presidential election to marry. Acting on the advice of Woodrow's political advisers, Edith and Woodrow kept their engagement a secret. They didn't want the president's enemies to turn the news into a scandal that might weaken his chances for reelection.

Later in the month, however, Edith changed her mind about postponing the wedding and told the family about their engagement. Knowing how the public would react to the news, Edith and Woodrow asked the family to keep the news quiet until they could inform the press. On October 7, the White House issued a press release informing the country of their engagement. The following morning, White House telephones were ringing off the walls.

In general, the public reacted favorably to the news of Wilson's engagement. Most people were only mildly curious about the new woman in his life. But some were asking troubling

The World Series

★ ★

When Edith and Woodrow attended the World Series opener in 1915, the series was a relatively new event. The National League (NL) had been playing baseball since 1876, and when the upstart American League (AL) was formed in 1901, it took the businessmen of baseball two years to adjust to a two-league sport. In 1903, the competing leagues agreed to coexist and to form a national commission that laid down the rules and regulations of the sport. At the same time, the friendly rivalry of the World Series was born. Barney Dreyfuss, owner of the NL champion Pittsburgh Pirates, challenged Henry Killilea, owner of the AL champion Boston Pilgrims, also known as the Red Sox, to a best-of-nine-games series. They played the first game in Boston on October 1, 1903, and the Pilgrims won the series 5 games to 3. In 1915, Boston beat Philadelphia 4 games to 1.

questions. Many people wondered whether the president had been involved with Edith before his wife Ellen had died. Amid all the publicity and mean-spirited gossip, Edith remained calm. She knew this was just the beginning of the treatment she could expect as the second wife of the most public figure in the United States.

Edith's first public appearance with the president came two days after their engagement was announced. She and her mother joined the president in Philadelphia for the opening of the World Series. Thereafter, Edith and Woodrow were often seen together and were frequently photographed as a couple.

CHAPTER FOUR

The Second Mrs. Wilson

* * * * * * * * * * * * * * *

Edith Galt and Woodrow Wilson were married in Washington, D.C., on December 18, 1915. A light snow had fallen the day before, providing the perfect background to their winter wedding. Edith wore a plain black velvet gown, a velvet hat, and orchids, her favorite flowers. All her life, Edith preferred to wear flowers, rather than jewelry. The president wore a black cutaway coat and gray striped trousers. They were a handsome couple, even though there was a great age difference between them. At the time, Edith was forty-three. Woodrow was only a few days short of being fifty-nine.

* * * * * * * * * * * * * * *

Woodrow and Ellen Wilson's daughters (left to right) Jessie, Margaret, and Nell

The Wilson Girls

✯ ✯

Born between 1886 and 1889, Woodrow and Ellen Wilson's three daughters grew up in a loving household surrounded by books, music, and encouragement. Loyal Margaret fiercely defended her younger sisters against schoolyard bullies and her father against negative election publicity. She grew up pursuing music and a great many causes. Traveling the world, she spent her last years in a religious colony in India. Jessie inherited her mother's beauty and was affectionately referred to by her father as one of the "proper Wilsons." She did very well at school and studied to become a teacher and missionary. She worked in Trenton at a settlement house for young women and strongly supported women's right to vote. National and world leaders attended her White House wedding to Frank Sayre. News of Jessie's first pregnancy cheered her mother's last pain-filled days. Eleanor (Nell) Wilson was always the closest to her father, sharing his sense of humor. The brunette of the family, she was considered quite beautiful and studied to become an illustrator. Her marriage to William McAdoo in 1914 caused quite a stir, partly because he was twice her age and partly because he was her father's secretary of the treasury.

Only immediate family members and a select group of cabinet members and White House staff attended the private wedding ceremony in Edith's home. Woodrow's three daughters were there. Nell and Jessie's husbands accompanied them. The president's sister was there also, as well as Ellen Wilson's brother Stockton. Attending from Edith's side of the family were her mother, all of her sisters and brothers and their husbands or wives. Edith's brother-in-law and sister-in-law from her first marriage were there, too. The presence of Dr. Grayson and Edith's best friend, Altrude Gordon, made the Wilsons' guest list complete.

After a brief ceremony and a light supper, Edith and Woodrow said good-bye to their guests and quickly depart-

Edith and Woodrow spent their honeymoon in Hot Springs, Virginia.

ed for their honeymoon. Assisted by Secret Service men, the newlyweds escaped bothersome reporters and sped away in a car. Not far from the city, they boarded a train for a two-week holiday in Hot Springs, Virginia. There, amid the glow of Christmas lights and the friendship of hotel well-wishers, the newlyweds relaxed and celebrated.

Early in January, Edith and Woodrow cut short their honeymoon and returned to the White House. German submarines were threatening to renew their attacks on merchant ships and it was more than likely that the United

This is one of the scenic views enjoyed by Edith and Woodrow during their honeymoon in Hot Springs.

States would be drawn into the war. While Woodrow focused on world problems, Edith dealt with personal matters. She sold her house on Twentieth Street and moved her belongings into the White House. Among the many things she brought to her new home were a piano, her favorite books, and her Wilcox and Gibbs sewing machine.

As First Lady, Edith immediately took charge of the White House staff and numerous social events. They were of little interest to her, however.

Terror on the High Seas

✮ ✮

On May 7, 1915, the British steamship *Lusitania,* enroute from New York to Liverpool, England, fell victim to a frightening new implement of war—the submarine. When a German submarine (called a U-boat) sank the luxury liner off the coast of Ireland, nearly 1,200 people died, including 128 Americans. The surprise attack on a civilian vessel enraged the American people. International law stated that the sea would be safe for those travelers not involved in a war. In August, the liner *Arabic* was sunk without warning, killing two Americans. At the outraged demands of President Wilson, the Germans ceased their attacks on passenger ships for several months. But when a French vessel, the *Sussex,* was sunk on March 24,

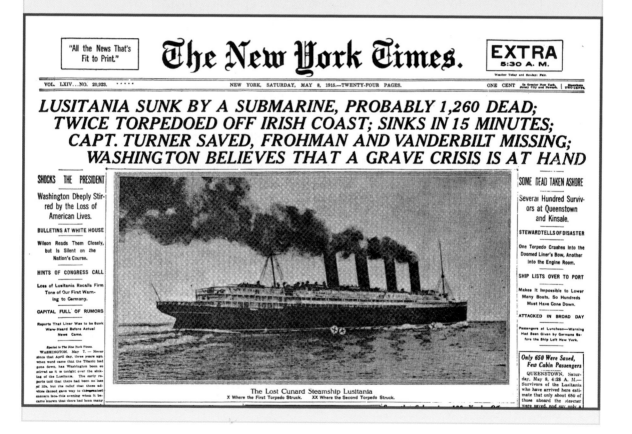

The New York Times.

EXTRA
5:30 A.M.

Weather Today and Sunday: Fair.

VOL. LXIV...NO. 20,923.   • • • • •   NEW YORK, SATURDAY, MAY 8, 1915.—TWENTY-FOUR PAGES.   ONE CENT   In Greater New York, Jersey City and Newark.   Elsewhere TWO CENTS.

LUSITANIA SUNK BY A SUBMARINE, PROBABLY 1,260 DEAD; TWICE TORPEDOED OFF IRISH COAST; SINKS IN 15 MINUTES; CAPT. TURNER SAVED, FROHMAN AND VANDERBILT MISSING; WASHINGTON BELIEVES THAT A GRAVE CRISIS IS AT HAND

SHOCKS THE PRESIDENT

Washington Deeply Stirred by the Loss of American Lives.

BULLETINS AT WHITE HOUSE

Wilson Reads Them Closely, but Is Silent on the Nation's Course.

HINTS OF CONGRESS CALL

Loss of Lusitania Recalls Firm Tone of Our First Warning to Germany.

CAPITAL FULL OF RUMORS

Reports That Liner Was to be Sunk Were Heard Before Actual News Came.

Special to The New York Times.
WASHINGTON, May 7.— Never since that April day, three years ago, when word came that the Titanic had gone down, has Washington been so stirred as it is tonight over the sinking of the Lusitania. The early reports told that there had been no loss of life, but the relief that these advices gave way to the greatest concern late this evening when it became known that there had been many

SOME DEAD TAKEN ASHORE

Several Hundred Survivors at Queenstown and Kinsale.

STEWARD TELLS OF DISASTER

One Torpedo Crashes Into the Doomed Liner's Bow, Another Into the Engine Room.

SHIP LISTS OVER TO PORT

Makes It Impossible to Lower Many Boats, So Hundreds Must Have Gone Down.

ATTACKED IN BROAD DAY

Passengers at Luncheon—Warning Had Been Given by Germans Before the Ship Left New York.

Only 650 Were Saved, Few Cabin Passengers

QUEENSTOWN, Saturday, May 8, 4:28 A.M.— Survivors of the Lusitania who have arrived here estimate that only about 650 of those aboard the steamer were saved, and say only a

The Lost Cunard Steamship Lusitania
X Where the First Torpedo Struck. XX Where the Second Torpedo Struck.

1916, injuring several Americans, the president threatened to break off all diplomatic relations with Germany. Germany agreed to stop the sinkings and did so until early 1917. Finally, on January 31, the Germans decided that unrestricted submarine warfare would help them win the war and announced that they would sink all ships, armed or unarmed, in the waters around Britain and France. This hostile action at last pushed the United States to enter World War I.

She preferred to be involved in her husband's concerns and created a position for herself as his assistant. Acting in this capacity, Edith shielded the president from people and mail he did not want to see. She made sure she was an active partner in every aspect of his daily routine.

Edith and Woodrow Wilson attended their first official function together as President and First Lady in March 1916.

CHAPTER FIVE

An Inseparable Team

✫ ✫ ✫ ✫ ✫ ✫ ✫ ✫ ✫ ✫ ✫ ✫ ✫ ✫ ✫ ✫

As a married couple, Edith and Woodrow were an inseparable team. In the White House, they began a daily routine of work and relaxation. Each morning, they awoke about six o'clock, ate a snack in their room, and then played golf. Edith believed that exercise was an important part of keeping the president relaxed and at his best.

At eight o'clock sharp, they ate a substantial breakfast together, then went to Woodrow's office where Edith helped him sign official documents. After the president signed each document, Edith blotted his signature. At nine o'clock, the president's private stenog-

✫ ✫ ✫ ✫ ✫ ✫ ✫ ✫ ✫ ✫ ✫ ✫ ✫ ✫ ✫ ✫

rapher arrived. Edith often stayed with the president and listened as he dictated his replies to all official business. Afterward, Edith turned to her own mail and the pressing problems of household management. There were endless lists of luncheons, dinners, and receptions that needed her approval, as well as numerous requests for invitations to the White House.

Edith worked with her husband at the president's desk each morning between eight and nine o'clock.

Around noon, Edith and Woodrow met for lunch. Later in the day, they often took a ride in the car before eating dinner at seven. Usually, more work followed, unless there were guests, or the Wilsons attended a vaudeville show.

Woodrow discussed everything with Edith. Talking about things helped him organize his thoughts. The discussions with Woodrow prompted Edith to read more. One of her goals was to read every book in Woodrow's extensive library. She hoped it would help her appreciate the meaning of historic events and better understand Woodrow's thinking. Then she would be able to talk about ideas more confidently and offer the president advice whenever he asked for it.

Some of the president's friends and closest political advisers were uneasy about his relationship with his wife. They thought the president was sharing too many government secrets with her. Matters he had previously shared only with his top aide, Colonel Edward House, or his private secretary, Joseph Tumulty, he now discussed with Edith. House and Tumulty be-

"A Woman's Century"

★ ★

By the time Woodrow Wilson became president, American women's lengthy struggle for *suffrage,* or the right to vote, was nearly over. In August 1920, the Nineteenth Amendment to the Constitution finally gave women the vote. The struggle had begun seventy-two years before at the first women's rights convention, held in Seneca Falls, New York. The women there had drawn up a manifesto called the "Declaration of Sentiments." It called for equality for women, including the right to vote. Over the years, the movement faced major opposition and was split by disagreement. Finally, in 1890, feminists united under the banner of the National American Woman Suffrage Association. The well-organized merger brought a spirit of unity to the movement, which plunged ahead toward suffrage. By 1920, it had 2 million members.

Between 1900 and 1920, women, more and more of them college educated, rushed to become involved in social causes of all kinds. Many, called *suffragists,* worked hard for the right to vote. Lobbying and marching for the cause, suffragists by the thousands made their voices heard. In January 1917, they picketed the White House hoping to convince the president to support their cause. Wilson eventually did support women's rights, as his first wife Ellen had. Surprisingly, while Ellen Wilson once observed that this would be "a woman's century," Edith strongly opposed the women's movement.

lieved that sharing top-secret information with her was risky and could affect the president's ability to make wise decisions. The president, of course, did not share their concerns.

Prior to meeting Woodrow Wilson and falling in love with him, Edith had thought mainly of her own interests. Afterward, however, her life centered on the president and his responsibilities. Woodrow had put meaning and purpose back into her life. His

President Woodrow Wilson (left) with his top aide, Colonel Edward House

Wilson (seated) and his private secretary, Joseph Tumulty

concerns and interests had become her own.

Altrude Gordon knew how much Edith's life had changed since she had met and married Woodrow Wilson. In a letter to Edith, Altrude wrote: You are "helping such a wonderful man— and so helping his work and the whole country. Those latent powers, abili-

ties, and charms of yours have found their opportunity—and are being used to such wonderful advantage and good purpose."

In January 1916, the president responded to the increased talk of U.S. involvement in World War I. Concerned that the country was unprepared for war, he decided to put in

World War I: Fast Facts

WHAT: The "Great War," the "War to End All Wars," the first truly global conflict

WHEN: 1914–1918

WHO: The Central Powers, including Austria-Hungary and Germany, opposed the Allied Powers, including Britain, France, and Russia. The United States entered the war on the Allied side in 1917.

WHERE: The Central Powers invaded Serbia, Romania, Russia, Belgium, France, and Italy. Fighting extended into the Atlantic Ocean and the Mediterranean Sea.

WHY: European disputes over land, economics, religion, and leadership boiled over in 1914 when Austrian archduke Francis Ferdinand was assassinated on a visit to Serbia. Austria declared war on Serbia, and other European nations picked sides. The United States got involved largely because German submarine warfare disrupted commerce in the North Atlantic Ocean.

OUTCOME: The Central Powers fell to the Allied Powers in 1918, and an armistice was signed on November 11. The map of Europe was redrawn and the League of Nations was founded to settle international disputes. Ten million soldiers, including 116,500 Americans, had died.

motion a plan to get it ready. First on the agenda was a train tour of the West, which immediately got underway. At numerous cities and towns across the nation, the Wilsons stopped to speak with citizens about the likelihood of going to war. Known as the "President's Preparedness Campaign," the trip proved very successful. Excited crowds listened intently to the

President Wilson, wearing a straw hat and carrying an American flag, marches in a "preparedness" parade in June 1916.

Women trumpeters get the attention of a street crowd during a "Wilson for President" rally.

president's message and offered him their support. To Edith, they responded with warmth and genuine interest. Because it was an election year, the trip also was a test of how much support the president could expect at the polls in the fall.

Shortly after Edith and Woodrow returned home, Altrude and Cary Grayson were married. After the wedding, Edith and Woodrow devoted themselves entirely to Woodrow's reelection campaign. Not wanting to run the president's campaign from the White House, the Wilsons moved to a house in Shadow Lawn, New Jersey. The Graysons, Joe Tumulty, Helen Bones, and Edith's brother Randolph joined them. Together, they helped run the campaign.

Wilson supporters jammed the voting booths on Election Day, Nov-

President Woodrow Wilson and First Lady Edith Wilson (center) pose for a picture with Woodrow's campaign managers outside the White House.

Wilson delivered his acceptance speech to a huge crowd at his Shadow Lawn, New Jersey, home.

Wilson waves his hat during a New York City presidential motorcade after the election of 1916.

ember 7, 1916. They were hopeful they would cast the necessary votes to keep the president in the White House for four more years. By late evening, however, the election was too close to call. The Republicans were claiming victory at ten o'clock when the president went to bed.

Edith was disappointed, yet secretly happy, with the election returns. She felt that now, she and Woodrow could finally have a life of their own. But when the final results of the election were tabulated three days later, they showed that Woodrow had been reelected by a slim margin of about a half-million votes. The news must have been difficult for Edith to accept. She knew that, with the country on the verge of war, the next four years would be much more difficult than the last.

President Wilson delivering his second inaugural address at the Capitol

Woodrow and Edith in an open car on Inauguration Day, 1917

Edith's Inaugural gown is on display at the Smithsonian Institution.

CHAPTER SIX

Surviving War and Peace

☆ ☆ ☆ ☆ ☆ ☆ ☆ ☆ ☆ ☆ ☆ ☆ ☆ ☆ ☆ ☆

Woodrow's second term in office began with a distressful decision. He had kept the United States out of the war with Europe as long as he could. Now, he must ask Congress to declare war on Germany and fight "to make the world safe for democracy."

On April 2, 1916, Congress unanimously supported the president's call to arms. The United States and more than twenty other countries formed an alliance, or a pact, called the Allied Powers. They promised to help one another stop Germany, Austria-Hungary, Turkey, and Bulgaria (the Central Powers) from killing innocent people and expanding their borders into other nations.

☆ ☆ ☆ ☆ ☆ ☆ ☆ ☆ ☆ ☆ ☆ ☆ ☆ ☆ ☆ ☆

President Wilson with an enlargement of the congressional resolution declaring war on the Imperial German Government

Sixty-fifth Congress of the United States of America;

At the First Session,

Begun and held at the City of Washington on Monday, the second day of April, one thousand nine hundred and seventeen.

JOINT RESOLUTION

Declaring that a state of war exists between the Imperial German Government and the Government and the people of the United States and making provision to prosecute the same.

Whereas the Imperial German Government has committed repeated acts of war against the Government and the people of the United States of America: Therefore be it

Resolved by the Senate and House of Representatives of the United States of America in Congress assembled, That the state of war between the United States and the Imperial German Government which has thus been thrust upon the United States is hereby formally declared; and that the President be, and he is hereby, authorized and directed to employ the entire naval and military forces of the United States and the resources of the Government to carry on war against the Imperial German Government; and to bring the conflict to a successful termination all of the resources of the country are hereby pledged by the Congress of the United States.

Champ Clark,
Speaker of the House of Representatives.

Thos. R. Marshall
Vice President of the United States and
President of the Senate.

Approved 6 April, 1917

Woodrow Wilson

The president asked Edith to play a vital role in the secret communication process conducted between the United States and other Allies. She translated the coded messages coming in from Europe for the president and coded the president's replies. As a result, Edith knew top-secret information about the war.

Edith became involved in the war in more visible ways, too. She and sev-

The front page of the New York Journal announced the declaration of war.

To save labor costs during the war, Edith brought in a flock of sheep to graze on the White House lawn.

eral cabinet wives cut spending and showed U.S. citizens how to save, or ration, items. The rationing of peace-time products allowed American factories to concentrate on producing products for the war. Edith put the White House on a budget. She and Woodrow cut their own monthly spending by $2,000.

To cut labor costs, Edith had a flock of sheep sent to the White House. Grazing on the lawn kept the grass short and eliminated the expense of a gardening crew. Workers also sheared the sheep and sold the wool to benefit the Red Cross. During this

A food-conservation pledge card signed by First Lady Edith Bolling Wilson

TO THE FOOD ADMINISTRATOR,
WASHINGTON, D. C.

I AM GLAD TO JOIN YOU IN THE SERVICE OF FOOD CONSERVATION FOR OUR NATION AND I HEREBY ACCEPT MEMBERSHIP IN THE UNITED STATES FOOD ADMINISTRATION, PLEDGING MYSELF TO CARRY OUT THE DIRECTIONS AND ADVICE OF THE FOOD ADMINISTRATOR IN THE CONDUCT OF MY HOUSEHOLD, INSOFAR AS MY CIRCUMSTANCES PERMIT.

Name. *Edith Bolling Wilson*

Address. *The White House*

Number in Household.................. Do you employ a cook?................

Occupation of Breadwinner............................

Will you take part in authorized neighborhood movements

for food conservation?... *Yes* ....

There are no fees or dues to be paid. The Food Administration wishes to have as members all of those actually handling food in the home.

DIRECTIONS

Mail your pledge card to the Food Administrator, Washington, D. C., and you will receive FREE your first instructions and a household tag to be hung in your window.

Upon receipt of ten cents with your pledge card and a return addressed envelope, the official button of the Administration, and if desired, the shield insignia of the Food Administration will also be sent you.

"Help Can't Wait"

✷ ✷

In 1881, the American Red Cross rose from the ashes of a forest fire. Since 1859, a movement in Europe had been stirring to organize an international body to care for wounded soldiers on the battlefield. Amazingly, no such group existed, and supporters proposed a nonmilitary volunteer organization that would not take sides and would be safe from attack. The United States refused to participate, however, not wanting to become involved in a European venture. Dismayed, nurse Clara Barton organized a Red Cross in the United States in 1881, hoping to change minds. Clara struggled with the cause until a huge forest fire in Michigan left thousands of people homeless and injured. Her fledgling group then raised $80,000 in relief money. Red Cross help after a flood along the Ohio River did the final convincing. In 1882, the United States joined Europe in its efforts to establish an International Red Cross. Today, the American Red Cross has approximately 1,650 chapters.

time, reporters and cartoonists often referred to Edith as "the shepherdess."

Edith also joined a Red Cross unit. Every day, she put on her striped and starched blue-and-white uniform and helped feed soldiers while they were waiting to leave for Europe. She set up a Red Cross unit at the White House where she, Helen Bones, and relatives sewed pajamas, pillowcases, and blankets for the soldiers.

To relax when the burdens of the war became too much for them, Edith and Woodrow exercised. Besides getting Woodrow to play golf, Edith had a billiard table installed in the White House, where the two of them frequently played. They also went horseback riding. The rides became a regular routine but never replaced their daily automobile rides.

While the war dragged on, the president wrote a peace plan. There were fourteen points in the plan, which he intended to be the foundation for peace talks between the Allies

"Knit Your Bit"

★ ★ ★ ★ ★ ★ ★ ★ ★ ★ ★ ★ ★ ★ ★ ★ ★ ★ ★ ★

As the country entered World War I, Americans pitched in as Edith did, knitting socks for soldiers and sewing pajamas for the wounded. Many volunteered to serve soldiers on their way to Europe at makeshift canteens in railroad stations. To conserve supplies, food, and energy, Americans endured endless rationing, cutting back on everything from coal to butter. Patriotic citizens observed "heatless, meatless, and wheatless" days. Since Germany led the world in producing fabric dyes, color disappeared from American clothing. Steel went into guns and tanks instead of women's corsets. Women wore lower heels in an effort to provide leather for military harnesses and belts. Cloth was conserved by eliminating outside pockets on men's suits. Youngsters hooted at anyone thoughtless enough to drive their cars on gasless Sundays, while diligent motorists hitched horses to their bumpers.

Wilson (with flag) marches in a 1917 Liberty Bond parade to raise funds for the war effort.

The Chicago Daily Tribune front page announces the end of World War I.

American soldiers in France celebrate the armistice.

A huge crowd in front of the White House waits to see President Wilson on Armistice Day, November 11, 1918.

Getting Back from Over There

✦ ✦

With the Armistice signed in November 1918, each Allied navy turned to serving the needs of its own nation. This left the United States Navy alone to transport home some 2 million American soldiers from the battlefields of Europe. The navy converted ships of all kinds into transport ships, expanding the fleet to four times its size on November 11. The commander of the American Expeditionary Forces, General John J. Pershing, demanded that the troops remain sharp, so drilling, exercise, and schooling continued throughout the long wait. Living in temporary camps, most of the men didn't return home until the spring or summer of 1919—nearly a year after the war's end.

New York City celebrated Armistice Day with a huge parade.

and the Central Powers at the end of the war. Finally, on November 11, 1918, Germany signed a truce, or armistice, with the Allies, and World War I officially came to a close.

After the armistice, Edith and Woodrow began making plans to attend the peace conference scheduled for January 18, 1919, in Paris, France. The president wanted to ensure that his Fourteen Points plan would be included in the peace settlement. His fourteenth point called for

The Wilsons arrived in Brest in December 1918, several weeks before the peace conference that was scheduled to begin on January 18.

Wilson (hatless) being driven through the streets of Paris on December 14, 1918

President Wilson is driven under a "Vive Wilson" banner that is stretched over this Paris street.

the establishment of a League of Nations, which was to be a peace-keeping body. It would protect any member nation that was attacked by another.

On December 4, 1918, the Wilsons, Dr. Grayson, and several of the president's advisers boarded the steamer *George Washington* in New York and sailed for Europe.

Having arrived in Europe early, the Wilsons spent several weeks visiting France, England, and Italy before the

conference began. For Edith, the European experience was like Cinderella's story. She and her prince were invited to balls in the castles of kings and queens.

In France, the Wilsons met Premier Clemenceau. They visited injured soldiers in American and French hospitals and American troops holed up in barns and temporary shacks. In London, crowds lined the streets and cheered them wildly as they went by. They were the guests of King George

President Wilson (fifth from left, seated) and Edith (third from left) have their 1918 Christmas dinner with French and American dignitaries at Montigny-le-Roi, France.

71

Woodrow (second from left) and Edith (right) with Britain's King George and Queen Mary on January 17, 1919

First Lady Edith Wilson (left) and Queen Mary during a carriage ride in London

"The Big Four" chat outside the Palace of Versailles near Paris where the peace conference was held. Left to right: Prime Minister David Lloyd George of Great Britain, Premier Vittorio Orlando of Italy, Premier Georges Clemenceau of France, and President Woodrow Wilson of the United States

and Queen Mary at Buckingham Palace. In Italy, they met with King Victor Emmanuel and attended receptions given in their honor. Italians considered President Wilson "the best friend of humanity" because he had helped bring an end to the Great War and had provided a plan for peace.

The United States was one of twenty-seven nations represented at the peace conference being held in the Palace of Versailles near Paris, France. Four leaders led the delegates attend-

ing the conference: President Wilson of the United States, Premier Georges Clemenceau of France, Prime Minister David Lloyd George of Great Britain, and Premier Vittorio Orlando of Italy. They were called "The Big Four."

On February 14, 1919, Edith and Dr. Grayson received permission to attend the historic conference. It was the day that President Wilson spoke on behalf of the League of Nations, and the delegates voted to include the league in the treaty draft. Non-

President Wilson stayed in this elaborately decorated suite during his trip to France for the peace conference.

The luxurious bedroom in Wilson's suite in France

delegates were not allowed in the room, so to avoid being seen by any of the delegates, Edith and Dr. Grayson sat behind heavy red brocade curtains in a small alcove. For nearly four hours, they remained motionless. Only when President Wilson spoke did they part the curtains slightly to see as well as hear him.

As Edith wrote in her memoirs, "It was a great moment in history, and as he stood there—slender, calm, and powerful in his argument—I seemed to see the people of all depressed countries—men, women and little children—crowding round and wait-

President Wilson leaves for his second trip to Paris to witness the treaty's ratification.

ing upon his words. He rarely made long speeches, and this was no exception. I could see it had made a great impression, and I longed to go to him and tell him all I felt."

After Wilson's speech, the delegates voted to include the league in the peace treaty. Satisfied with the progress that had been made in Versailles, the Wilsons sailed for Washington. The president was going to present the peace treaty to the Senate. Without U.S. support of the treaty, and especially the League of Nations, peace in Europe would not last.

If the league survived and grew in strength, future wars might be avoided. Then all the lives that were lost in the Great War would have some meaning. And the president would have "kept the faith with the people," particularly with the soldiers who had sacrificed so much.

Shortly after returning to Washington, the president presented the Treaty of Versailles to the Senate and asked them to ratify it without any changes. While the Senate studied the treaty and discussed its many points, the Wilsons returned to Paris to wit-

The Big Four (President Woodrow Wilson in center) doffed their hats to cheering crowds after the Treaty of Versailles was signed on June 28, 1919.

ness its ratification in Europe. They arrived in Paris in mid-March 1919, only to learn that opponents of the league had managed to get it omitted from the treaty. Shocked by the news, Woodrow vowed to get the support he needed to get the league back in.

Edith and Woodrow rented a house in Paris. They converted a section of it into conference rooms for the president's work on the peace treaty. Daily, the Big Four met to hammer out points of the treaty. For the next four months, work continued well into the night. Often on the verge of a nervous breakdown, the president was confined to his bed several times. Under Edith's loving care, however, he managed to finish what he had set out to do. On June 28, 1919, President Wilson completed a revised peace treaty that France, England, and Italy could support. Now it needed to be accepted, or ratified.

The trip to Europe had brought Edith and Woodrow closer than ever.

President Wilson received this Pierce Arrow automobile when he returned from his 1919 trip to Europe.

A partner in everything Woodrow did, Edith knew how important the league was to him and how critical it was in preventing future wars. She had suffered with her husband while he fought to gain support for the treaty and to establish a League of Nations. She would continue fighting with him to get the treaty approved.

Throughout the difficult months, Edith's belief in her husband and his message never wavered. She must have felt, however, that the job was ruining her husband's health and shortening their remaining time together. She could see the president's condition growing worse with each passing day.

★ ★ ★ ★ ★ ★ ★ ★ ★ ★ ★ ★ ★ ★ ★

CHAPTER SEVEN

For Love and Honor

* * * * * * * * * * * * * * * * * * *

After returning from Europe, Edith began working with Woodrow to persuade the United States Senate to ratify the treaty and become a member of the League of Nations. Many in the Senate opposed the treaty because it included the league. They believed that if the United States became a member of the League of Nations, it would have the heaviest responsibility to solve world problems. Many politicians did not want the United States to get involved.

To win support for the league, the president turned to the American people. On September 3, 1919, he, Edith, and Dr. Grayson boarded the presidential train

* * * * * * * * * * * * * * * * * * *

The Wilsons in Bismarck, North Dakota, during their tour to win support for the League of Nations

Edith and Woodrow on the presidential train in Missouri during the nationwide tour

and set out on a nationwide speaking campaign to win support for the league. The twenty-two-day trip was nonstop and intense. On the evening of September 25, the exhausted president took ill. Complaining of severe headaches and unbearable pain, he collapsed.

All night, Edith remained at his bedside. Years later, she wrote about this incident in her memoirs: "As I sat there watching the dawn break slowly, I felt that life would never be the same; that something had broken inside me; and from that hour on I would have to wear a mask—not only to the public but to the one I loved best in the world; for he must never know how ill he was, and I must carry on."

In the morning, Edith saw that one side of Woodrow's face was disfigured and that he couldn't see out of one eye. He spoke with great difficulty. Unable to carry on, the president can-

President Wilson leans over the train rail to shake hands with a supporter of the League of Nations during the 1919 tour of the country.

Woodrow speaking in San Diego, California, during the 1919 trip

81

Treaties are agreements made by two or more nations that, like a contract between people, binds the countries by law to certain terms. Treaties can end wars or establish global rules for dealing with a variety of common concerns such as the environment. The U.S. Constitution gives treaty-making power to the president, but the Senate must approve a treaty before the United States is bound by its terms. The Treaty of Versailles was signed by all parties except the United States to end World War I. President Wilson could negotiate the Treaty of Versailles, but without the Senate's ratification, the United States remained technically at war with Germany. In fact, it wasn't until July of 1921 that Congress passed a resolution "ending" the war. The treaty-making process is a good example of the system of checks and balances that keeps any one of our three branches of government from having too much power. Not all treaties are negotiated by the president in person. Usually, the State Department hammers out treaty terms and then submits them to the Senate for approval by a two-thirds vote of the members present.

celed the trip, and the train returned to Washington.

Shortly after his return, the president suffered a stroke, which paralyzed his left side. Although the stroke damaged his thinking, the doctors believed that the president would get better if he got absolute rest.

On October 3, a day after the president suffered his stroke, the French Chamber of Deputies overwhelmingly ratified the Treaty of Versailles. The British had ratified it earlier.

A little more than a month later, the U.S. Senate voted against ratifying the treaty. Although the League of Nations was eventually established in Europe, it lacked direction and power without the United States as a member. It never functioned as Wilson had intended.

During the remaining year and a

Legacy of the League

★ ★

The League of Nations had a spotty record of achievement throughout its twenty-seven-year existence. Many of the countries that played the largest roles in World War I did not remain members for very long, and the league's ability to enforce its decisions was weak. It was, however, the first worldwide organization for settling international disputes. As a forerunner of today's United Nations, which took over the league's responsibilities in 1945, it played an important part in introducing the nations of the world to the possibilities of cooperation and intervention in times of conflict. Today, 185 countries belong to the United Nations, which meets in New York City and has peacekeeping forces at work in many "hot spots" around the world.

President Wilson (center) with his cabinet, 1917

half of the president's term in office, Edith and his cabinet members handled his affairs. Although Edith wanted her husband to resign from the presidency and get the complete rest that he needed, his doctors advised against it. The doctors believed resignation would only weaken the president's will to live. Instead, they suggested that Edith reduce the president's workload. She should inspect all the communications going to the president—tele-

Still a Killer

★ ★ ★ ★ ★ ★ ★ ★ ★ ★ ★ ★ ★ ★ ★ ★ ★ ★ ★ ★

Only the very intimate family circle knew that President Wilson suffered from arteriosclerosis, or hardening of the arteries. With such a condition already weakening his circulatory system, it is not surprising that the pressures of politics and an incredibly grueling work and travel schedule brought on first a thrombosis and then a stroke. A *thrombosis* occurs when fibrous material and blood platelets clot together inside an artery or vein and block the flow of blood. When such a clot forms in the brain, cells starved for oxygen quickly deteriorate or die, causing paralysis of whatever part of the body those brain cells control. This is termed a *stroke*. Today, stroke is the third leading cause of death in the United States after heart disease and cancer.

phone calls, documents, letters, and memos—and decide how the White House staff could act upon them. Only those matters the president absolutely had to see should be shown to him. The rest could wait.

Except for Dr. Grayson, there was no one else in the White House Edith felt she could trust to act in her husband's behalf. So, for Woodrow's sake, Edith accepted the difficult responsibility the doctors had asked of her. In her memoirs, she wrote: "I studied every paper, sent from the different Secretaries or Senators, and tried to digest and present in tabloid form the things that, despite my vigilance, had to go to the President. I, myself, never made a single decision regarding the disposition of public affairs. The only decision that was mine was what was important, and what was not, and the very important decision of when to present matters to my husband."

Dr. Grayson handled the reporters and the staff while Edith dealt with the business of the White House. At the heart of everything she and Dr. Grayson did was their desire to protect the president and help him

President Wilson presiding over the last meeting of his cabinet before leaving office

The Wilsons moved into this Washington, D.C., house on S Street in 1921.

recover. Edith spent most of each day with the president, limiting official business to a few minutes a day. This forced the staff and members of Congress to handle business on their own. Edith made no policy decisions. She usually referred matters to appropriate cabinet members, while letting issues of minor importance wait.

With Edith's help, the president slowly recovered. However, he never regained his strength, and his inability to function well forced him to face the fact that he could not run for a third term. With retirement in mind, Edith and Woodrow talked about where they would live when they moved out of the White House. After much discussion, they decided to remain in Washington, D.C. It was Edith's home, and Woodrow could do research at the Library of Congress for the next book he intended to write.

In December 1920, the Wilsons bought a house in the 2300 block of S Street. While Edith focused all her

Wilson (left) and Warren Harding on their way to the Capitol for Harding's inauguration as president

On Armistice Day 1921, the Wilsons waved to thousands of visitors at the house on S Street.

attention there, Woodrow spent his time preparing the White House for the incoming president, Warren Harding. It was a busy three months. Woodrow turned sixty-four, Edith and Woodrow celebrated their fifth wedding anniversary, and another chapter in their lives was coming to a close.

On March 4, 1921, the Wilsons welcomed President and Mrs. Harding to the White House. After posing for a few pictures at the Capitol, the Wilsons went to their new house on S Street. Edith had arranged the furni-

ture to look like their living quarters in the White House. She even had a duplicate made of the Lincoln bed that Woodrow had slept in.

For the next three years, the Wilsons spent a great part of each day answering the letters that poured in. They got help from Edith's brother Randolph, who had been hired as their personal secretary. On many afternoons, they entertained politicians and other guests. Helen Bones and Woodrow's three daughters often came to stay with them. Edith's family

Woodrow and Edith leave their house to go for a drive to celebrate Armistice Day 1921.

This photograph of Woodrow, in his customary top hat and using a cane, was taken in 1921.

Florence Kling Harding (1860–1924)

✦ ✦

Florence Kling Harding

A native of Marion, Ohio, spunky Florence Harding followed Edith Wilson as First Lady in 1921. Warren Harding was her second husband; a first marriage had ended in divorce. Editor of the local newspaper, Warren married Florence in 1891. She went to work for him and proved herself to be a woman of good business sense. In 1915, the Hardings moved to Washington where Warren served in the Senate and then as president. As First Lady, the savvy newspaperwoman Florence greeted the press enthusiastically. She made herself more available to them than any First Lady before her. She was a strong supporter of women's equality and minority rights, but her primary concern was for wounded World War I veterans. Like Edith, Florence counseled her president husband in matters of state and politics. While he called her the Duchess, some people called her Madame President because of her influence. Florence lived only a year after the sudden death of President Harding, who died while in office. She spent much of her final year destroying Harding's presidential papers, afraid that they might be misunderstood in light of several scandals that had plagued his administration.

and the Graysons were also frequent visitors. Occasionally, Edith accompanied Woodrow to public appearances and helped him with his writing. Usually, however, they stayed away from the public, protecting their private lives as much as possible.

Whenever Woodrow insisted that Edith spend some time by herself, she played cards with a few of her friends or went to the theater. However, Woodrow's health continued to fail, and as he lay dying, she never left his bedside.

☆ ☆ ☆ ☆ ☆ ☆ ☆ ☆ ☆ ☆ ☆ ☆ ☆ ☆

CHAPTER EIGHT

Life without Woodrow

✯ ✯ ✯ ✯ ✯ ✯ ✯ ✯ ✯ ✯ ✯ ✯ ✯ ✯ ✯

Woodrow Wilson died quietly on February 3, 1924. For Edith it was a devastating loss. Woodrow had brought love and joy to her life. He had given it meaning. Without him, she felt a terrible emptiness. After Woodrow's death, it took Edith more than a year to let go of her grief and rebuild her life.

In 1939, Edith wrote a book about her life called *My Memoir*. The dedication reads: "To My Husband Woodrow Wilson who helped me build from the broken timbers of my life a temple wherein are enshrined memories of his great spirit which was dedicated to the service of his God and humanity."

✯ ✯ ✯ ✯ ✯ ✯ ✯ ✯ ✯ ✯ ✯ ✯ ✯ ✯ ✯

Woodrow's coffin being carried from the house on S Street to the National Cathedral

While Woodrow lived, Edith did her best to protect him and keep him well. After his death, she dedicated herself to preserving his memory. She authorized his biography and actively helped in getting friends to contribute their letters and experiences for the book. Whenever she traveled, she presented herself as Woodrow Wilson's widow. She attended events honoring his memory and promoted causes he supported. Each time she went to Europe, she sat in on a session of the League of Nations. She was director of

Edith (second from right) at a 1932 League of Nations dinner in Philadelphia

Edith helps to lay the cornerstone of the Woodrow Wilson School of Public and International Affairs.

Edith (seated) with Bess Truman (left) and Eleanor Roosevelt at a 1955 Democratic party dinner

pany of other politicians' wives, she attended many gatherings and was frequently seen in Washington's inner circles. She was the president's guest at the December 8, 1941, session of Congress, when Roosevelt declared war on Japan and officially entered World War II. Twenty years later, she was still included in presidential events. In 1961, she rode in President John Kennedy's inaugural parade. A few months later, she sat beside him in the White House as he authorized the building of the Woodrow Wilson Memorial. It was Edith Wilson's last public appearance.

Edith had planned to attend Vir-

the Woodrow Wilson Foundation to promote international cooperation. She also worked tirelessly to make the Wilson birthplace at Staunton, Virginia, a national shrine.

During President Franklin Roosevelt's Administration, Edith was a familiar figure in the White House and in the Senate gallery. In the com-

Edith (right) watches as President John F. Kennedy authorizes the Woodrow Wilson Memorial.

Portrait of America, 1961: New Frontiers

☆ ☆ ☆ ☆ ☆ ☆ ☆ ☆ ☆ ☆ ☆ ☆ ☆ ☆ ☆ ☆ ☆ ☆ ☆ ☆

Months before her death in December 1961, Edith Wilson attended the inauguration of President John F. Kennedy. During his speech, President Kennedy challenged Americans: "Ask not what your country can do for you. Ask what you can do for your country." Kennedy launched a lively new era, calling it the New Frontier. It gave us the Peace Corps, the space race, and the Twist.

It also gave us a powerful civil-rights movement. Across the 50 states, 18 million African-Americans were still struggling for the equal rights promised them after the Civil War during Reconstruction. In 1961, blacks and whites called Freedom Riders organized nonviolent sit-ins, boycotts, and marches against segregation across the South. They often met with violence, arrest, and bloodshed, but they exposed the shame of segregation and discrimination.

Another tough challenge in 1961 was the Cold War. Many Americans feared the threats of communism and nuclear attack. As leader Fidel Castro embraced communism in nearby Cuba, President Kennedy took strong steps. With support

On January 1, 1962, Edith Wilson's coffin was carried into the National Cathedral for funeral services and burial beside her husband.

from the United States, Cuban exiles invaded the island in an attempt to over-throw Castro. The mission failed disastrously, and Castro remains in power today.

Meanwhile, American teens discovered their own new frontiers, energized by the rock 'n' roll of Elvis Presley. Rocker Chubby Checker taught Americans to do the Twist. At home, television offered something for everyone. *American Band-stand* debuted all the new music, and *Dr. Kildare* made medicine glamorous. Cow-boys shot 'em up in popular Westerns like *Gunsmoke*, *Wagon Train*, and *Rawhide*. Game shows and comedies, variety shows and cartoons jammed the airwaves. More people read *TV Guide* than any other magazine in America, except *Reader's Digest*. But thinking Americans began to realize television's dangers, especially for children. The head of the FCC called it a "vast wasteland."

Perhaps the best measure of 1961, however, was a 230-mile (370-km) trip taken by one Alan Shepard Jr. in July. Shepard's journey took him 115 miles (185 km) straight up into space atop a fiery missile and then dropped his tiny Mercury capsule safely into the sea by parachute fifteen minutes later. Although a Russian had already orbited the earth, Shepard's feat as the first American "astronaut" helped define the country's newest frontier.

ginia's 105th anniversary celebration of Wilson's birth on December 29, 1961. In his honor, the government was dedicating the Woodrow Wilson Bridge over the Potomac River. However, the day before Woodrow's birth-day, Edith died in her sleep.

As Woodrow Wilson's most vigi-lant protector and strongest supporter in life, Edith Bolling Galt Wilson saw to it that the world remembered his accomplishments and carried on his ideals. Together, their lives furthered the spread of world peace.

☆ ☆ ☆ ☆ ☆ ☆ ☆ ☆ ☆ ☆ ☆ ☆ ☆ ☆ ☆

The Presidents and Their First Ladies

President	Birth–Death	First Lady	Birth–Death
YEARS IN OFFICE			
1789–1797			
George Washington	1732–1799	Martha Dandridge Custis Washington	1731–1802
1797–1801			
John Adams	1735–1826	Abigail Smith Adams	1744–1818
1801–1809			
Thomas Jefferson†	1743–1826		
1809–1817			
James Madison	1751–1836	Dolley Payne Todd Madison	1768–1849
1817–1825			
James Monroe	1758–1831	Elizabeth Kortright Monroe	1768–1830
1825–1829			
John Quincy Adams	1767–1848	Louisa Catherine Johnson Adams	1775–1852
1829–1837			
Andrew Jackson†	1767–1845		
1837–1841			
Martin Van Buren†	1782–1862		
1841			
William Henry Harrison‡	1773–1841		
1841–1845			
John Tyler	1790–1862	Letitia Christian Tyler (1841–1842)	1790–1842
		Julia Gardiner Tyler (1844–1845)	1820–1889
1845–1849			
James K. Polk	1795–1849	Sarah Childress Polk	1803–1891
1849–1850			
Zachary Taylor	1784–1850	Margaret Mackall Smith Taylor	1788–1852
1850–1853			
Millard Fillmore	1800–1874	Abigail Powers Fillmore	1798–1853
1853–1857			
Franklin Pierce	1804–1869	Jane Means Appleton Pierce	1806–1863
1857–1861			
James Buchanan*	1791–1868		
1861–1865			
Abraham Lincoln	1809–1865	Mary Todd Lincoln	1818–1882
1865–1869			
Andrew Johnson	1808–1875	Eliza McCardle Johnson	1810–1876
1869–1877			
Ulysses S. Grant	1822–1885	Julia Dent Grant	1826–1902
1877–1881			
Rutherford B. Hayes	1822–1893	Lucy Ware Webb Hayes	1831–1889
1881			
James A. Garfield	1831–1881	Lucretia Rudolph Garfield	1832–1918
1881–1885			
Chester A. Arthur†	1829–1886		

† wife died before he took office   ‡ wife too ill to accompany him to Washington   * never married

1885–1889			
Grover Cleveland	1837–1908	Frances Folsom Cleveland	1864–1947
1889–1893			
Benjamin Harrison	1833–1901	Caroline Lavinia Scott Harrison	1832–1892
1893–1897			
Grover Cleveland	1837–1908	Frances Folsom Cleveland	1864–1947
1897–1901			
William McKinley	1843–1901	Ida Saxton McKinley	1847–1907
1901–1909			
Theodore Roosevelt	1858–1919	Edith Kermit Carow Roosevelt	1861–1948
1909–1913			
William Howard Taft	1857–1930	Helen Herron Taft	1861–1943
1913–1921			
Woodrow Wilson	1856–1924	Ellen Louise Axson Wilson (1913–1914)	1860–1914
		Edith Bolling Galt Wilson (1915–1921)	1872–1961
1921–1923			
Warren G. Harding	1865–1923	Florence Kling Harding	1860–1924
1923–1929			
Calvin Coolidge	1872–1933	Grace Anna Goodhue Coolidge	1879–1957
1929–1933			
Herbert Hoover	1874–1964	Lou Henry Hoover	1874–1944
1933–1945			
Franklin D. Roosevelt	1882–1945	Anna Eleanor Roosevelt	1884–1962
1945–1953			
Harry S. Truman	1884–1972	Bess Wallace Truman	1885–1982
1953–1961			
Dwight D. Eisenhower	1890–1969	Mamie Geneva Doud Eisenhower	1896–1979
1961–1963			
John F. Kennedy	1917–1963	Jacqueline Bouvier Kennedy	1929–1994
1963–1969			
Lyndon B. Johnson	1908–1973	Claudia Taylor (Lady Bird) Johnson	1912–
1969–1974			
Richard Nixon	1913–1994	Patricia Ryan Nixon	1912–1993
1974–1977			
Gerald Ford	1913–	Elizabeth Bloomer Ford	1918–
1977–1981			
James Carter	1924–	Rosalynn Smith Carter	1927–
1981–1989			
Ronald Reagan	1911–	Nancy Davis Reagan	1923–
1989–1993			
George Bush	1924–	Barbara Pierce Bush	1925–
1993–			
William Jefferson Clinton	1946–	Hillary Rodham Clinton	1947–

Edith Bolling Galt Wilson Timeline

1872	★	Susan B. Anthony is arrested for trying to vote
		Ulysses S. Grant is reelected president
		Yellowstone National Park becomes the first U.S. national park
		Edith Bolling is born on October 15
1873	★	Economic depression spreads throughout the United States
1877	★	Rutherford B. Hayes becomes president
1879	★	Women win the right to argue cases before the Supreme Court
1880	★	James A. Garfield is elected president
1881	★	James A. Garfield is shot and dies about three months later
		Chester A. Arthur becomes president
		American branch of the Red Cross opens
1882	★	Congress approves a pension for widows of U.S. presidents
1884	★	Grover Cleveland is elected president
1885	★	Washington Monument is dedicated
1886	★	President Cleveland dedicates the Statue of Liberty
1888	★	Benjamin Harrison is elected president
1889	★	Flood in Johnstown, Pennsylvania, kills 2,295 people
1891	★	Populist Party is formed
1892	★	Ellis Island immigration center opens
		Grover Cleveland is elected president
1893	★	Women's suffrage is adopted in Colorado
		Economic depression hits the United States

1894	★	Labor Day is made a holiday
1896	★	Edith Bolling marries Norman Galt
		William McKinley is elected president
		First moving pictures are shown in New York City
		First Ford automobile is built in Detroit
		First modern Olympics are held in Athens, Greece
1898	★	Spanish-American War is fought, resulting in the United States annexing Puerto Rico, Guam, and the Philippines
1900	★	William McKinley is reelected president
1901	★	President McKinley is assassinated
		Theodore Roosevelt becomes president
1903	★	Wright brothers fly their airplane for the first time
		First World Series is played
		Edith Bolling Galt's only child is born and dies within three days
1904	★	Theodore Roosevelt is elected president
1906	★	Theodore Roosevelt receives the Nobel Peace Prize
1908	★	William Howard Taft is elected president
		Norman Galt dies
1909	★	National Association for the Advancement of Colored People (NAACP) is founded
1912	★	Woodrow Wilson is elected president
		Titanic sinks in the North Atlantic
1913	★	Sixteenth and Seventeenth Amendments are added to the Constitution
		Henry Ford sets up his first assembly line
1914	★	Panama Canal is completed
		World War I begins
1915	★	*Lusitania* is sunk by a German submarine
		Edith Bolling Galt marries Woodrow Wilson
1916	★	Woodrow Wilson is reelected president

99

1917	★	United States enters World War I
1918	★	United States and its allies win World War I
1919	★	Eighteenth Amendment is added to the Constitution
		Woodrow Wilson helps write the Treaty of Versailles
		U.S. Senate refuses to ratify Treaty of Versailles
		Woodrow Wilson receives the Nobel Peace Prize
1920	★	Nineteenth Amendment, which gave women the right to vote, is added to the Constitution
		Warren G. Harding is elected president
1922	★	First woman is appointed to the U.S. Senate
		Lincoln Memorial is dedicated
1923	★	President Harding dies
		Calvin Coolidge becomes president
1924	★	Calvin Coolidge is elected president
		Woodrow Wilson dies
1927	★	Charles Lindbergh flies solo across the Atlantic Ocean
1928	★	Herbert Hoover is elected president
		Amelia Earhart becomes the first woman to fly across the Atlantic Ocean
1929	★	Stock market crashes, which starts the Great Depression
1931	★	"The Star-Spangled Banner" becomes the national anthem
1932	★	Amelia Earhart becomes the first woman to fly solo across the Atlantic Ocean
		Franklin D. Roosevelt is elected president
1933	★	Twentieth and Twenty-first Amendments are added to the Constitution
		President Roosevelt begins the New Deal
1934	★	Scientist at the DuPont Company invents nylon
1935	★	Congress passes the Social Security Act
1936	★	Franklin D. Roosevelt is reelected president

1939	★	World War II begins
		Edith Wilson writes *My Memoir*
1940	★	**Franklin D. Roosevelt is reelected president**
1941	★	Japanese bomb Pearl Harbor
		United States enters World War II
1944	★	**Franklin D. Roosevelt is reelected president**
1945	★	President Roosevelt dies
		Harry S. Truman becomes president
		Germany surrenders to the Allies in Europe
		United States drops atomic bombs on Japan
		Japan surrenders, ending World War II
1947	★	**Jackie Robinson becomes the first African-American to play major-league baseball**
1948	★	Harry S. Truman is elected president
1949	★	**United Nations headquarters is dedicated in New York City**
1950	★	United States enters Korean War
1951	★	**Twenty-second Amendment is added to the Constitution**
1952	★	Dwight D. Eisenhower is elected president
1953	★	**Korean War ends**
1954	★	Supreme Court declares segregated schools to be unconstitutional
1956	★	**Dwight D. Eisenhower is reelected president**
1960	★	John F. Kennedy is elected president
1961	★	**Edith Wilson rides in President Kennedy's inaugural parade**
		First Americans fly in space
		United States sends aid and advisers to South Vietnam
		Twenty-third Amendment is added to the Constitution
		Edith Wilson dies on December 29

Fast Facts about Edith Bolling Galt Wilson

Born: October 15, 1872, in Wytheville, Virginia

Died: December 29, 1961, in Washington, D.C.

Burial Site: National Cathedral, Washington, D.C.

Parents: William Holcombe Bolling and Sallie White Bolling

Education: Educated at home by parents, grandmother, tutors, and governesses until 1887; boarding school in Abingdon, Virginia (1887); Powell's School in Richmond, Virginia (1889–1890)

Career: Operated the Galt jewelry and silver business after her husband's death

Marriages: To Norman Galt in 1896, until his death in 1908; to Woodrow Wilson on December 18, 1915, until his death in 1924

Children: One child, a baby boy, who lived only three days in September 1903

Places She Lived: Wytheville, Virginia (1872–1889); Richmond, Virginia (1889–1890); Washington, D.C. (1890–1961)

Major Achievements:

* ✴ Created position of assistant to the president to shield him from people and mail he did not want to see (1916).
* ✴ Helped run her husband's reelection campaign (1916).
* ✴ Translated coded messages from the European allies and coded President Wilson's replies during World War I.
* ✴ Cut the White House budget and showed U.S. citizens how to ration during World War I.
* ✴ Also had sheep graze on the White House lawn to eliminate gardening expenses.
* ✴ Traveled to Europe after World War I, attended the peace conference at Versailles, and worked to gain support for the peace treaty in the United States.
* ✴ Handled presidential affairs during her husband's illness (1919–1920).
* ✴ Wrote *My Memoir* (1939), authorized a biography of her husband, sat in on sessions of the League of Nations when she traveled to Europe, served as director of the Woodrow Wilson Foundation, and worked to make the Woodrow Wilson Birthplace in Virginia a national shrine.

Fast Facts about
Woodrow Wilson's Presidency

Terms of Office: Elected in 1912 and 1916; served as the twenty-eighth president of the United States from 1913 to 1921

Vice President: Thomas Riley Marshall (1913–1921)

Major Policy Decisions and Legislation:
- Formally recognized the Republic of China (1913).
- Signed the Underwood Tariff Act (1913), which reduced tariffs by 10 to 26 percent.
- Signed act that established the U.S. Coast Guard (1915).
- Asked Congress for a declaration of war and received it (April 1917), which brought the United States into World War I.
- Set down Fourteen Points as the basis for a peace settlement when the war ended (1918).
- Helped write the Treaty of Versailles that included a League of Nations, and urged the American people and the U.S. Senate to support the treaty (1919).

Major Events:
- President Wilson held the first press conference in the White House and agreed to meet the press twice a week (1913).
- The Sixteenth (1913), Seventeenth (1913), Eighteenth (1919), and Nineteenth (1920) Amendments were added to the U.S. Constitution.
- The Panama Canal was completed (1914).
- President Wilson appointed and the U.S. Senate confirmed three associated justices to the U.S. Supreme Court: James Clark McReynolds (1914), Louis Dembitz Brandeis (1916), and John Hessin Clarke (1916).
- World War I (1914–1918) took place in Europe, with the United States entering the war in 1917.
- The czar of Russia was overthrown and the Communists gained control of Russia's government (1917).
- President Woodrow Wilson was awarded the Nobel Peace Prize (1919).

Where to Visit

The Capitol Building
Constitution Avenue
Washington, D.C. 20510
(202) 225-3121

Museum of American History of the Smithsonian Institution
"First Ladies: Political and Public Image"
14th Street and Constutution Avenue, N.W.
Washington, D.C.
(202) 357-2008

National Archives
Constitution Avenue
Washington, D.C.
(202) 501-5000

The National First Ladies Library
The Saxton McKinley House
331 South Market Avenue
Canton, Ohio 44702

White House
1600 Pensylvania Avenue
Washington, D.C. 20500
Visitor's Office: (202) 456-7041

White House Historical Association
740 Jackson Place, NW
Washington, D.C. 20503
(202) 737-8292

Woodrow Wilson Birthplace and Museum
18–24 North Coalter Street
Staunton, Virginia 24401
(703) 885-0897

Online Sites of Interest

The First Ladies of the United States of America

http://www2.whitehouse.gov/WH/glimpse/ firstladies/html/firstladies.html

A portrait and biographical sketch of each First Lady plus links to other White House sites

Internet Public Library, Presidents of the United States (IPL POTUS)

http://www.ipl.org/ref/POTUS/

An excellent site with much information on Woodrow Wilson, including personal information and facts about his presidency; many links to other sites including biographies and other Internet resources

The National First Ladies Library

http://www.firstladies.org

The first virtual library devoted to the lives and legacies of America's First Ladies; includes a bibliography of written material by and about the nation's First Ladies and a virtual tour, with pictures, of the restored Saxton McKinley House in Canton, Ohio, which houses the library

The White House

http://www.whitehouse.gov/WH/Welcome. html

Information about the current president and vice president; White House history and tours; biographies of past presidents and their families; a virtual tour of the historic building, current events, and much more

The White House for Kids

http://www.whitehouse.gov/WH/kids/html/ kidshome.html

Includes information about White House kids, past and present; famous "First Pets," past and present; historic moments of the presidency; and much more

The Woodrow Wilson Birthplace and Museum

http://www.elpress.com/staunton/ BRTHPLC.HTML

A site that contains photos of the stately house in Staunton, Virginia, that is a National Historic Landmark, as well as a description of the contents of the museum and gift shop

For Further Reading

Dolan, Edward F. *America in World War I*. Brookfield, Conn.: Millbrook Press, 1996.

Giblin, James Cross. *Edith Wilson: The Woman Who Ran the United States*. Women of Our Time series. New York: Viking Press, 1992.

Gormley, Beatrice. *First Ladies*. New York: Scholastic, Inc., 1997.

Gould, Lewis L. (ed.). *American First Ladies: Their Lives and Their Legacy*. New York: Garland Publishing, 1996.

Jacobson, Doranne. *Presidents and First Ladies of the United States*. New York: Smithmark Publishers, Inc., 1995.

Klapthor, Margaret Brown. *The First Ladies*. Washington, D.C.: White House Historical Association, 1994.

Kummer, Patricia K. *Washington, D.C.* One Nation series. Mankato, Minn.: Capstone Press, 1998.

Mayo, Edith P. (ed.). *The Smithsonian Book of the First Ladies: Their Lives, Times, and Issues*. New York: Henry Holt, 1996.

Osinski, Alice. *Woodrow Wilson*. Encyclopedia of Presidents series. Chicago: Children's Press, 1989.

Sandak, Cass R. *The Wilsons*. First Families series. New York: Crestwood House, 1993.

Stewart, Gail B. *World War I*. America's Wars series. San Diego: Lucent Books, 1991.

Tribble, Edwin (ed.). *A President in Love: The Courtship Letters of Woodrow Wilson and Edith Bolling Galt*. Boston: Houghton Mifflin, 1981.

Wilson, Edith. *My Memoir*. North Stratford, N.H.: Ayer Company Publishers, 1980.

Index

Page numbers in **boldface type** indicate illustrations

107

Photo Identifications

Cover: Portrait of First Lady Edith Bolling Galt Wilson by Adolpho Muller-Ury
Page 8: Edith Galt about two months before her marriage to Woodrow Wilson
Page 12: Edith Bolling at about fifteen years old
Page 22: Edith Bolling in 1896 at the time of her engagement to Norman Galt
Page 34: Edith Bolling Galt with Woodrow Wilson at the 1915 World Series in Philadelphia
Page 44: Portrait of Edith Bolling Galt Wilson at about the time of her marriage to Woodrow Wilson
Page 52: President Woodrow Wilson and First Lady Edith Wilson on the White House lawn, 1916
Page 62: A 1920 portrait of First Lady Edith Wilson by Seymour Stone
Page 78: Portrait of Edith Wilson by Adolpho Muller-Ury
Page 90: Photograph of Edith Wilson taken in 1949

Photo Credits©

About the Author

Alice Flanagan lives in Chicago, Illinois, and writes books for children for a variety of publishers. She credits her interest in history and her love of reading to her parents, who are avid readers and history buffs. Once a teacher, Ms. Flanagan knows the importance of having good books to stimulate reading and learning. Through her writing, she tries to provide those books and encourage an enthusiastic curiosity about life.

Ms. Flanagan has written many books for Children's Press. *Edith Bolling Galt Wilson* is her second title in the Encyclopedia of First Ladies series. Other titles include *Dolley Payne Todd Madison* and *Ellen Louise Axson Wilson*. Ms. Flanagan has written three titles in the Encyclopedia of Presidents series: *Andrew Jackson*, *Woodrow Wilson*, and *Franklin D. Roosevelt*. She has written numerous titles in the popular True Book series. Among her more recent titles is a five-book set on Native Americans: *The Pueblo*, *The Zuni*, *The Ute*, *The Shawnee*, and *The Wampanoag*.

Ms. Flanagan is also author of more than fifteen titles in the Our Neighborhood series for the primary grades. She likes this series because she had the opportunity to interview the people she wrote about. Also, she enjoyed working with her sister and her husband, who provided the photographs for this photojournalistic approach to career biographies.

Ms. Flanagan hopes young readers will like her book on Edith Bolling Galt Wilson and be encouraged to find out more about Edith Wilson and other women who influenced history.